What Makes You Special?

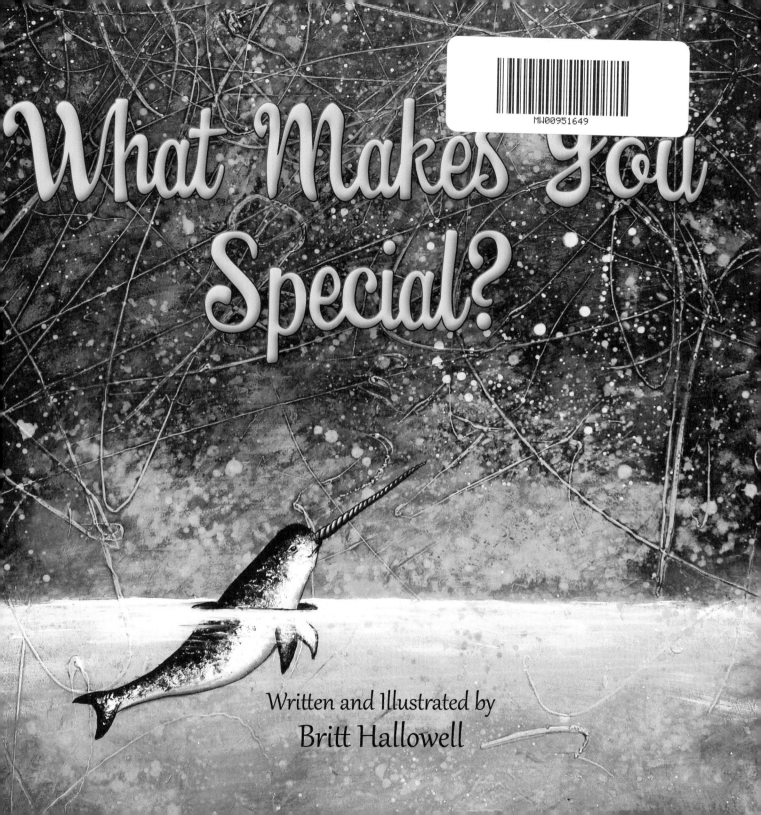

Written and Illustrated by
Britt Hallowell

One day, as Little Narwhal and Papa were swimming, Little Narwhal noticed they were different from the other whales who were playing nearby.

"Papa," he asked, "why do we have a horn? The other whales don't have one."

Papa smiled, "It's not a horn... it's a tooth. It helps us find food in the dark ocean."

Little Narwhal looked at the other whales again. "I don't like being different," he sighed sadly.

"Being different is wonderful!" Papa replied. "We are all unique in our own way. Belugas are the only white whales. They are very slow but can swim backwards. Killer whales aren't really whales at all – they are the biggest dolphins! They can't smell, but they can hear very well. Being different is what makes us special!"

Little Narwhal was curious to know what made others special and decided to set out on an adventure. He was heading toward the shore when he was surprised to see a bird underwater!

"What are you doing here?" he asked.

"I'm a puffin," said the bird. "I can fly *and* swim."

"My papa says being different makes us special. That's *very* special!" remarked Little Narwhal.

Sea because I can be rather clumsy, but it makes others smile, so I don't mind."

Little Narwhal said goodbye and continued on his journey.

Soon Little Narwhal reached the shore where he met a moose.

"Hello Moose. My papa says being different makes us special. How are you special?"

"Oh, I'm very special," said the old moose. "I could use a pair of glasses because I can't see well. I'm also missing front teeth. Although," Moose added proudly, "I'm the largest deer in the world, and I absolutely love to swim. I can even swim underwater!"

"That *is* special! Thank you!" said Little Narwhal and he continued on his journey.

Soon, Little Narwhal spotted an arctic fox.

"Hello Fox. My papa says being different makes us special. How are you special?"

"I have very small legs and ears," replied the fox. "But that helps keep me warm. I wrap my fluffy tail around me like a blanket. I also have one brown and one blue eye."

"That *is* special! Thank you!" said Little Narwhal and he continued on his journey.

Suddenly a snowy owl flew by.

"Hello Owl. Why are you awake? Don't you know it's daytime?" asked Little Narwhal.

"Silly whale," responded the owl. "I'm not nocturnal. I sleep at night like you."

"My papa says being different makes us special. What makes you special?"

The owl said, "I can see very far away. I can't move my eyes, but I can turn my head almost completely around!"

"That *is* special! Thank you!" said Little Narwhal and he continued on his journey.

Soon Little Narwhal met a baby harp seal.

"Hello Seal. My papa says being different makes us special. How are you special?"

The seal replied, "My mama says my white fur helps me blend into the snow. It absorbs sunlight during the day to keep me warm at night. One day when I learn to swim, I will have a silver coat like she does to help me hide in the water."

"That *is* special!" said Little Narwhal.

"It's getting dark," the seal pup yawned. "I should be getting to bed."

Little Narwhal thought he should head home too.

On his way back, Little Narwhal met a mama and baby polar bear.

"Hello Polar Bears. My papa says being different makes us special. What makes you special?"

The mama polar bear replied, "Did you know our fur is not really white? Each hair is a clear tube that reflects light, which makes us look white. Our skin is really black."

The baby bear added proudly, "And I can swim really far! I'm an excellent swimmer!"

Little Narwhal said, "That *is* special! Thank you," and he continued home.

Little Narwhal had almost reached his home when he saw a musk ox at the water's edge.

"Hello Musk Ox. My papa says – *PEE YEW*!!! What's that smell?!" he exclaimed.

"Sorry," said the Musk Ox. "That's me. I can't help it, I'm just very stinky. But that thick, smelly wool can be turned into yarn. Some say it's the warmest and softest wool there is! So that makes me special!"

Little Narwhal agreed then hurried home as he heard Papa call his name.

"Welcome home," Papa said. "What have you learned today?"

"Oh Papa!" Little Narwhal smiled, "I learned that whether we are big, small, white, black, young, old, have one giant tooth, are missing teeth, or even if we are really, *REALLY* smelly, we all have a purpose and are special just the way we are! Being different really *is* special!"

Papa laughed, hugged Little Narwhal close, and said, "You'll always be the most special to me."

Want to know more...?

Read on for even more interesting facts about arctic animals!

Arctic Fox

- Even though it has small ears, an arctic fox has excellent hearing. They can hear small animals under the snow, then use their front feet to punch through the snow to find food.

- Foxes will sometimes follow polar bears to eat their scraps. There has even been a case of a polar bear and fox becoming "friends" and playing together.

- Arctic foxes mate for life and both parents help take care of the babies.

- Baby foxes are called pups.

- Families live in underground dens called burrows.

- Arctic foxes are omnivores, which means they will eat meat as well as plants f food. Lemmings, mice and berries are their favorite foods.

- They wrap their tails around themselves like a blanket to keep warm during th cold arctic winters, but they have the best insulated fur of any mammal, so it takes a lot to mak them cold. They even have fur on their paws to keep their feet warm.

- Arctic foxes can have multiple colored eyes (that's called heterochromia).

- Their fur changes color from white in the winter to brown in the summer for camouflage, and co double in length during the winter months for warmth.

Bald Eagle

- The bald eagle is the national bird of America.

- Both male and females have brown bodies and white heads (hence the name "bald" eagle).

- Like most birds, the females are bigger than males.

- Eagles mate for life and both males and females help incubate the eggs.

- Babies are born with soft white feathers and don't get their adult feathers unt they are about 5 years old.

- Eagles can't smell but they can taste and are known as rather picky eaters.

- Their talons are 10 times stronger than human hands and their eyesight is 4 times better than ours!

- Surprisingly, bald eagles can swim! Sometimes they try to catch a fish that is too big for them and end up having to swim with the fish to shore.

Beluga

- Belugas are the only all white whale species and one of the smallest. They are born all gray and become white after about 8 years.

- They are the only cousin to the narwhal. They are the only members of the whale family "Monodontidae" who have teeth and no dorsal fins.

- They swim slowly, but can swim backwards.

- The beluga's neck vertebrae are not fused, so it can turn its head in all directions, unlike other whales who must turn their whole bodies.

- Belugas are very social animals. They usually live in groups of 2 to 10 but can travel in groups up to several thousand!

- Belugas are the most vocal whale. They can chirp, click, whistle and even mimic laughter. They are called the "canaries of the sea" because of their musical sounds.

- Belugas are thought to be one of the most intelligent animals on earth due to their brain size.

Caribou

- Caribou and reindeer are the same species, but caribou are wild and reindeer are domesticated.

- Domesticated reindeer usually have shorter legs than wild caribou.

- They are herd animals and live in groups of 100 to 250,000!

- Caribou are the only member of the deer family whose females also grow antlers.

- Every year they shed their antlers and grow new ones.

- They have a special bone in their nose that warms the air they breathe before it reaches their lungs. Basically they never breathe cold air even in the winter.

Harp Seal

- Harp seals are sometimes called saddleback seals because of the dark, saddle-like marking on the backs of the adult seals.
- Baby seals are called pups. They are born without blubber but quickly gain weight while nursing.
- Baby seals start out yellow, then turn white and furry after 3 days, then eventually silver and smooth.
- Pups and their mothers recognize each other by smell.
- Once a year, seals return to land to mate and molt. Molting is when they lose their fur and grow a new coat.

- Seals are warm blooded, so they need a lot of blubber and fat to keep them warm in the freezing waters.
- They can stay underwater for 15 minutes.
- Harp seals are carnivores and eat mainly fish, squid, seabirds and shellfish.
- Harp seal are known as "earless seals". Technically they do have ears, but they just aren't visible from the outside.

Moose

- Moose are the largest deer and the second largest land animal in North America (second only to the bison).
- Male moose are called bulls and females are cows. Babies are called calves.
- Moose love to swim and can even swim underwater! They are also very fast runners and can run up to 35 MPH.
- Only males have antlers. They lose their antlers every year and grow new antlers in the spring. Antlers are covered in velvet at first and then become shiny late in the year.
- They are very solitary creatures and rarely seen with other animals.

- They eat around 60 pounds of food every day!
- Moose are near sighted (which means they can't see far away) and don't have upper front teeth. Not having front teeth makes it easier for them to suck underwater plants into their mouth.
- Moose have very powerful kicks. Very few predators will try to attack a moose!

Musk Ox

Musk ox have long shaggy hair which is very smelly, especially for males. Hence the name "musk" ox.

Their wool coat is used for coats and blankets and is said to be one of the softest and warmest wools in the world.

Although they look much like cows, they are actually more closely related to sheep and goats.

Both males and females have horns that resemble a hat. Females have hair between their horns though and the male's horns are connected at the top.

Musk ox don't chew their food, they just swallow it whole, but later they spit that up and chew on it like cows do. It's called "chewing their cud".

Musk ox are herd animals who live in groups up to 60 with one male leading the other males and one female in charge of the other females. When in danger, all the adults form a circle around the babies to act like a protective wall.

Narwhal

The narwhal's recognizable horn is actually a very long tooth. This tooth has tons of nerve endings that help narwhals find food and direction as well as sense pressure changes in the ocean.

Usually only males have the long tooth but sometimes females can too.

Sometimes they can even have two!

Narwhals live in pods of 10 to 20 whales.

Like the beluga, they have teeth and no dorsal fin.

They can stay underwater for up to 25 minutes.

The myth of the unicorn is due in part to the narwhal. Viking sailors would cut off a narwhal tooth and sell it in other parts of the world claiming it was the magical unicorn's horn.

Orca
(Killer Whale)

- Are commonly called killer whales, although technically they are the largest dolphins and not really "true" whales.
- Orcas stay with their moms all their lives and live in groups called pods.
- Females lead the pods and can have anywhere from 3 to 100 members.
- Each pod has its own call and is usually made up of family members.
- Orcas are recognizable by their black and white coloring and huge dorsal fin.
- Orcas are found all over the ocean. In fact, they are the most widely distributed mammals across the world aside from humans.
- They can't smell but can hear better than most animals. Orcas use echolocation to "smell".
- Orcas cannot actually sleep or else they would drown. When they rest, only half of their brain shuts down and the other half remains awake. They always have one eye open to go to the surface to breath. This is true of all dolphins and whales.

Polar Bear

- Polar bears are the largest member of the bear family and the largest land carnivore.
- Polar bear's hair is not really white. Each hair is a hollow, clear tube that reflects light which makes them appear white. This helps them blend into surroundings and also retain more warmth.
- The skin of a polar bear is actually black.
- Polar bears are excellent swimmers. They can swim for 100 miles.
- They have the thickest fur of any bear and 4 inches of fat under their skin, which helps keep them warm in the freezing waters.
- Their favorite food is seal.
- Polar bears do not hibernate, but are active year round.
- Male polar bears can stand almost 10' tall. That's almost two humans on top of each other!
- Sadly, polar bears are endangered due to climate change. Warmer temperatures means less ice and less ice means less food for polar bears.

The beak and feet of puffins change color throughout the year. They become brightly colored in the spring and summer then dim during the winter months.

Puffin

Puffins are called the "clown of the seas" and "sea parrots".

Puffins spend most of the year living on the sea. They have waterproof feathers and can sleep floating on the water.

When on land, they live in burrows. They are very clean animals and even have a separate "toilet" area in the burrow.

Puffins can fly in the sky and also "fly" underwater. They flap their wings to swim and use their feet like rudders to steer.

They mate for life and both parents care for the babies.

Puffins are very tiny. They are only 10" tall and weigh only about as much as a soda can.

A puffin's beak is uniquely shaped and allows them to hold around 10 fish at a time.

Like other sea birds, puffins can drink saltwater. Their bodies process the salt out through their nostrils.

Otters are members of the weasel family.

Otters are very playful animals. They love to roll and flip underwater.

Sea Otter

They are very resourceful animals as well. They use rocks like hammers to smash open clam shells to eat the soft insides.

Otters are very social. Groups of otters in the water are called "rafts". There can be up to 100 otters in a raft.

Otters sleep floating on the water. While sleeping, otters will hold hands with other otters or wrap themselves in kelp to keep from floating away.

When in the water, otter's nostrils and ears close to keep water out.

Otters don't have fat, but trap air under their fur to keep warm.

They also have retractable front claws.

Otters have "pockets" of loose skin above their forearms to store food they catch while swimming. They also keep their favorite rock here so it's always nearby if they find clams or mussels that need opened.

Snowy Owl

- The snowy owl is one of the largest and heaviest North American owl species.
- For being such a large owl, it has small eyes compared to other owl species.
- Males become all white with age and females are spotted and brown
- Snowy owls mate for life.
- Snowy owls are diurnal, which means they mainly hunt during the day instead of being nocturnal like most owls.
- They live in places without many trees, so they build nests on the grou
- Females sit on the eggs while the male brings her food.
- They are very protective of their nests and will even fight off wolves to protect their babies.
- Owls can turn their heads 270 degrees, which is three quarters of the way around! They can't actually move their eyes, so it comes in hand being able to swivel their heads so far!

Walrus

- There are two species of walrus: the Atlantic and Pacific walrus.
- Like the moose, females are called cows and males are called bulls. Both males and females have tusks. Males can have tusks up to 3' long!
- Their tusks are very big teeth. These teeth never stop growing for the walrus' entire life. You can tell a walrus' age by the size of its tusks.
- They use their tusks to pull themselves out of the water, to break ice and find food, and also to fight other walruses.
- The most aggressive walrus in the group is the leader.

- Walruses are very fat and blubberous. They can weigh up to 1.5 tons, which is the size of a sm car.
- The walrus' mustache is very sensitive and is used to help find food on the dark ocean floor. T mustache has up to 450 whiskers.
- A walrus can slow its heartbeat down to help conserve heat as well as stay underwater longer can hold its breath for half an hour. They can even fall asleep underwater!

To Quinn: you brighten my every day
To all my other cheerleaders: thank you for encouraging me to
reach for the stars
-BH

About the Author

Britt Hallowell is an award winning artist featured in advertising campaigns, galleries, restaurants and personal collections around the world. *What Makes You Special?* is her debut children's book, which she wrote and illustrated based on her original painting titled *Wishing on Stars: the Unicorn of the Sea*, which features the hero of the story, Little Narwhal. Britt lives outside of Columbus, Ohio with her husband and daughter. She loves painting, spending time with family, creating and traveling. Visit brittsfineart.com to see more art.

Paperback edition
ISBN 978-0-9988521-1-9
1 2 3 4 5 6 7 8 9 10

The art for this book was created by the author with acrylic paint, plaster, charcoal pencil, oil pastels, and ink pen on wood.
Original paintings can be found at brittsfineart.com
Printed in China

CPSIA information can be obtained at www.ICGtesting.com
Printed in the USA
LVIW01n0945290318
571578LV00001BA/2